AUTUMN
PUBLISHING

Published in 2022
First published in the UK by Autumn Publishing
An imprint of Igloo Books Ltd
Cottage Farm, NN6 0BJ, UK
Owned by Bonnier Books
Sveavägen 56, Stockholm, Sweden
www.autumnpublishing.co.uk

0122 001
2 4 6 8 10 9 7 5 3 1
ISBN 978-1-80022-273-1

Written by Marnie Willow
Illustrated by Mike Henson
Edited by Helen Catt
Designed by Richard Sykes

Printed and manufactured in China

Climate Neutral
Product

I CAN
SAVE
THE
WORLD!
AUTUMN
PUBLISHING

I can **SAVE THE WORLD!**

I've got this secret, see?

Sometimes what this planet needs is a . . .

SUPER KID like me.

SWOOSH!
I can
SAVE THE WORLD!
I start with something small.
Some super-fast recycling . . .
CLANG!
CRASH!

. . . And a light
off in the hall.
CLICK!

We've only got

ONE WORLD,

so I think before I choose
fairer fruit or chocolate:
I check the pack for clues.

I REDUCE AND I REUSE,

because small choices can be drastic.
Fewer bags and bottles
means a lot less brand new plastic.

I can
SAVE THE WORLD!
The seas and rivers too.
WHOOSH!

NIP!

I'll clean up all
the rubbish,
so the water's

**CLEAR
AND
BLUE!**

We can

SAVE THE WORLD!

We'll try not to choose the car.

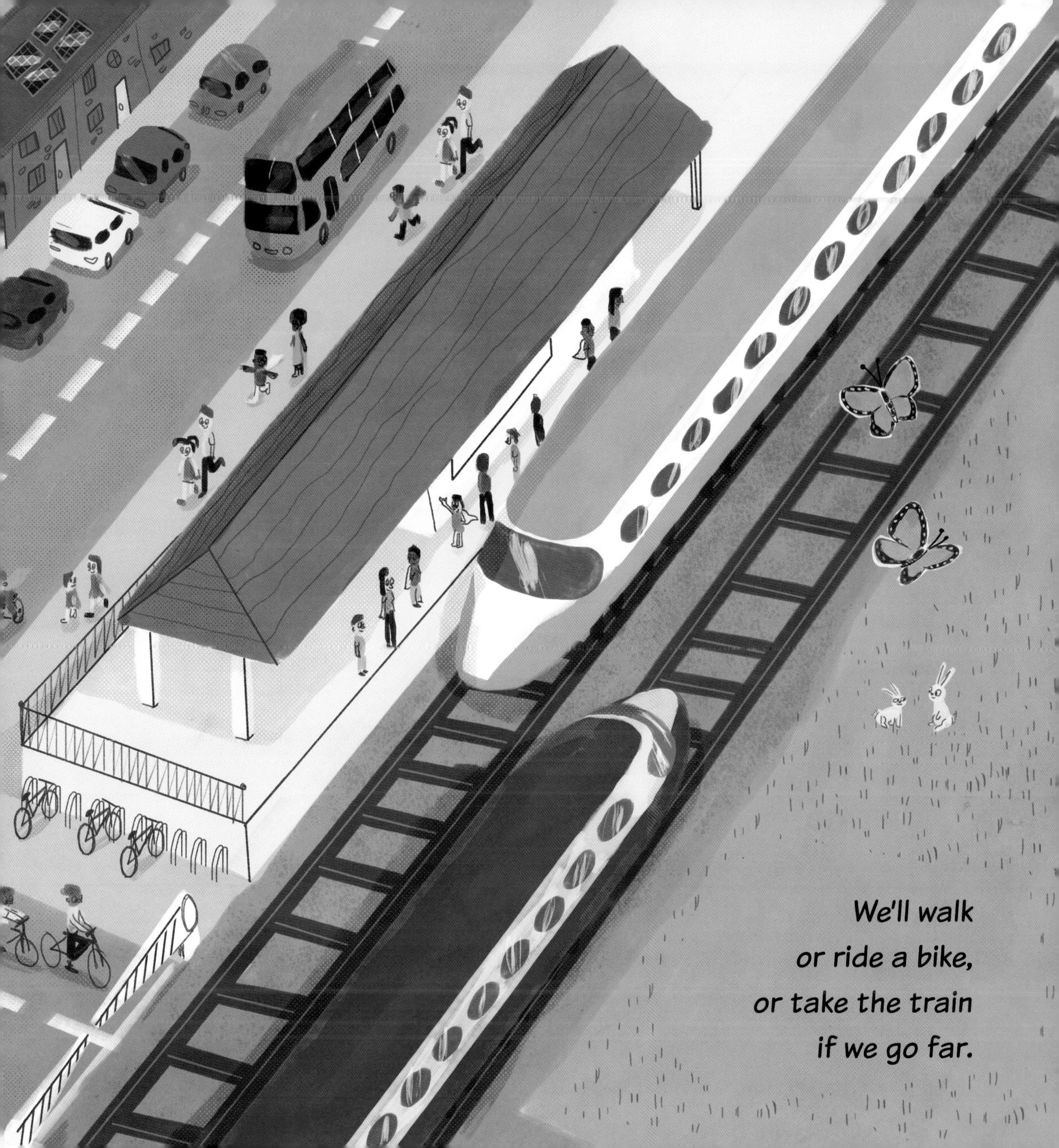

We'll walk
or ride a bike,
or take the train
if we go far.

I can
SAVE
THE
WORLD!
I won't throw good food out.

If I SNIFF...

. . . and find it whiffs,

it's compost for my sprouts.

I can

SAVE THE WORLD!

But I can't do it all alone.

It takes a lot of
heroes to make a
garden grow.

Sometimes all it takes
is just one candle in the night.

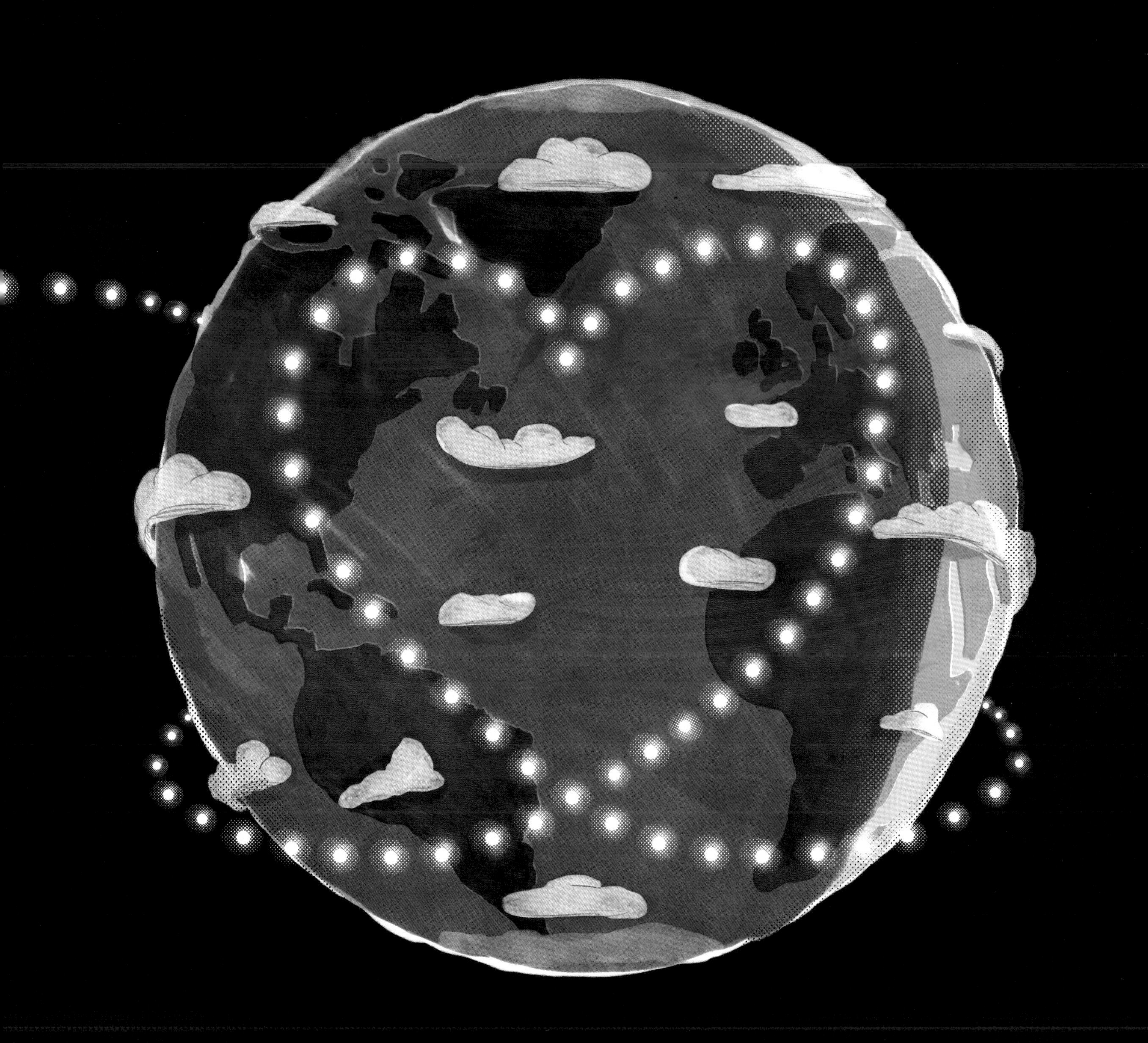

One candle lights one more
And soon the world is set alight.

I can

CHANGE THE WORLD!

Lots of people have before.

When we all stand together,

WE'RE TOO BIG TO BE IGNORED.

I can **SAVE THE WORLD!**

My secret is, you see . . .

. . . it turns out lots of people have a secret

JUST LIKE ME!

WAYS TO CHANGE THE WORLD

Changing the world is a huge job, and no single person can do it alone. However, if lots of people work together, there are lots of things we can do to help look after the environment, to protect this amazing planet and the people and animals who live here. Here are some ideas:

Save energy around the house. Switch off lights and electronics when you're not using them.

Reduce the number of new things that you buy, and reuse whatever you can instead of buying new things.

Remember to recycle. Recycling turns old rubbish into useful things, so it doesn't go to landfill.

Swap reusable things for single-use plastics, like tote bags instead of plastic bags, or beeswax wrap instead of plastic film.

Choose chocolate, fruit and other foods that have been grown in a way that looks after our planet's wild spaces, including its rainforests and oceans.

Grow your own food if you can! It's fun, healthy and good for the environment.

Join or kickstart community projects like beach cleans, litter picks or community gardens to help look after the wild spaces around your home.

Get involved with bigger protest movements, whether that's joining a kid-friendly demonstration or writing letters to big companies and governments.